MAGNIFICENT WORDS TO LIVE BY

**By Hamilton Brower
and
Annette Parker Martin**

Published by
ARKETT PUBLISHING
division of Arkettype
PO Box 36, Gaylordsville, CT 06755
860-350-4007 • Fax 860-355-3970
www.arkett.com

To order additional copies of this book and posters, please visit:
www.magnificentwordstoliveby.com

Printed in USA

This book is dedicated to Pierce Merrick Brower. In his six short years, he embraced all that these pages are about.

It is also dedicated to our mothers, Mason Brower and Peg Parker. These wonderful women taught us to work hard, laugh harder, love fully, and to appreciate the abundant joys in life.

A's for ambition, a thing that you'll find

Begins in your heart and then enters your mind.

A feeling of wanting to be a success:

Achieve more where others accept so much less.

It lives in your heart and it makes you work more;

It makes you work hard, because that's what it's for.

Ambition's not something you buy or you learn,

Or borrow from someone then later return.

You can't see or touch it, nor can you fake it

And once it's inside you, no one can take it.

Ambition is something that gives you the fire

To work for whatever it is you desire.

B is for brave: an expression of might,

When inside what's felt is foreboding and fright.

The brave may have doubts, but they set them aside,

And tackle what's daunting, then end up with pride.

The brave do not falter or give in to fear.

They don't turn and flee because problems appear.

Their lives are defined by such words as heroic,

Steadfast and valiant, unswerving and stoic.

For you to be brave you must know in your head

It's best to confront what it is that you dread.

Brave does not mean that you're never afraid.

But rather than fear, it's your strength that's displayed.

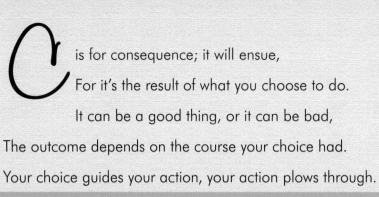

C is for consequence; it will ensue,

For it's the result of what you choose to do.

It can be a good thing, or it can be bad,

The outcome depends on the course your choice had.

Your choice guides your action, your action plows through.

A wave that affects all the lives close to you.

It can be quite gentle, a calm little bump,

Right over it even a child could jump.

Or a tsunami with such a big break.

It crushes the lives that it leaves in its wake.

So think of the consequence before you choose.

When choice comes to action, ensure you don't lose.

D is for dignity. It's something like pride.

It's goodness and self-respect felt deep inside.

Nobility's present; a sense of self-worth.

You earn it in life; it's not given at birth.

There's no need to brag when there's greatness in you.

It's evident in all you say and you do.

You humbly convey well-deserved self-esteem.

Your splendid behavior declares you supreme.

You've manners and poise, and you hold your head high.

You're able to look the world straight in the eye.

Decorum's one thing by which you are defined.

You're friendly and civil, polite and refined.

E is for effort. It helps get things done.

It turns out results. Or it leaves you with none.

Effort takes work, and it comes at a cost.

You'll pay with your energy, strength may be lost.

You'll have to be patient, for effort takes time.

But there's no better way to achieve the sublime.

You can't wait for others, it's all up to you

To discover the vastness of things you can do.

Completing a task, if your outcome is poor,

Examine your effort, then next time, give more.

Exhibiting effort shows that you intend

To achieve great success; it's the means to your end.

F is for focus. That's when you intend
To center your sight on a specified end.
Attention is given to only one item.
Your task becomes clearer ad infinitum.
It isn't the number of things you get done,
But how perfectly awesomely you can do one

That sets you apart from the everyday crowd.
So keep to your task and do all you've avowed.
We all have one thing at which we could be great
If only we'd focus and just concentrate.
When others work to drive you to distraction,
Focus will help you keep your course of action.

G is for generous: Those who are giving.

Those who are gracious in how they are living.

While some give their money – philanthropists do.

The giving of time is quite generous, too.

Donations of money help charities grow.

The lonely might need just a simple "hello."

When you lend a hand to a person in need,

You might find it pleasing to do that good deed.

Behaving with kindness is one way to give.

Displaying concern is a good way to live.

To give of yourself and to share what you can

Will benefit you and help your fellow man.

H stands for honor, displaying respect.
A show of esteem is the wanted effect.

A tribute that's given to those who stand out.

A good reputation is what it's about.

It's also a code that can serve as a guide.

A standard of decency upheld with pride.

You honor commitments by keeping your word.

You honor your life when you live undeterred.

It's not always easy and may take a toll.

But the way that you act is within your control.

When living with honor is what you desire

Supreme admiration is what you'll acquire.

I is for imagination, a portal in your mind.

Where real life and fantasy are easily entwined.

Think of places you can travel, think of things to do.

Think of things of wonder, things of awe that marvel you.

Think of things that others might have never thought before.

Think new ways of doing things; think that, and then think more.

Don't listen to the critics who can't comprehend your view.

Those lacking creativity should not unsettle you.

Do not allow the boring to restrain what you create.

Imagine something different – that's what leads to something great.

Remember, when you want to boost your life a little more,

Imagination's all you need. Now open up that door.

J is for just. It means to be fair.

It's moral correctness you strive to declare.

The principles guiding the just person through

Are decency, honor, and truthfulness, too.

All sides of an issue are taken to heart,

And being impartial's the way that you start.

When guided by reason you'll find what is true.

Relying on facts is important to do.

To stand by your ethics you may have to fight.

For not every person will do what is right.

When you are unbiased in choosing a side

It's clear to the world – only truth you'll abide.

K is for kindness, it leads to compassion,

A manner of conduct that's always in fashion.

It's gentle behavior displayed with finesse

By generous souls that convey thoughtfulness.

It's showing concern when another's in pain,

And offering help though you've nothing to gain.

Obliging and friendly are qualities of

The kindhearted person who demonstrates love.

When kindness is shown to somebody in need

Each person involved benefits from the deed.

If kindness and friendship are values you share

Then those all around you will know that you care.

17

L stands for loyal. It means being true,

Supportive and constant, and trustworthy, too.

When you remain faithful to friend and ideal

Respect in yourself is the sense that you'll feel.

To pledge your allegiance, you must choose a side

For loyalty cannot be spread far and wide.

The loyal don't waiver when choices emerge.

In bad times their loyalty will not diverge.

Discover those others who think as you do

And let them discover the loyal in you.

On loyalty everyone knows to depend.

It's something you'll find in the heart of a friend.

M's for moderation, it's a beneficial goal.

It shows restraint and discipline; it leads to self-control.

Restricting what you're longing for is not an easy charge

When everybody else, it seems, is living much too large.

But when your goal in life becomes to have more than you need,

It goes beyond necessity and can turn into greed.

It's wonderful to have big dreams and strive for great success,

But when the longing overwhelms you, make yourself want less.

It's healthier to find some satisfaction with "enough."

You never need to own, or eat, or covet excess stuff.

When bigger, better, faster, more in daily life won't cease,

A little moderation may enhance your inner peace.

N's for negotiate. A process you'll need
To ensure in the end all involved have agreed.
The result is the place where your focus should be,
But the choices you make on the way are the key.
You must give up a little, the others do, too.
That's the process you follow, it's just what you do.
Then when all is complete and the end is in sight
What you've done is cooperate, making things right.
Though you may not achieve every part of your dream,
There is peace to be found when you work as a team.
When you're working with others, it's vital to see
It is not about ME. No. It's all about WE.

O stands for opinion. It's your view, to be exact.

It may be based on sentiment; it may be based on fact.

You'll need more than emotion and ideas you just sense,

To give your view a strong and justifiable defense.

It's best when you observe and fully understand what's true,

And not just have a feeling for beliefs that come from you.

New data will combine with old perceptions in your mind;

The old and new unite, and your opinion's what you find.

You draw your own conclusion so, in theory, you're not wrong.

But having facts to back you up will make your viewpoint strong.

When you take time to contemplate all that you see and hear,

You'll offer an opinion that is balanced and sincere.

P's for perseverance, it's what keeps you in the game.

Where others want to just give up, you never do the same.

Your path may be quite hard at times, your progress may be slow.

You know just what it is you want, so on and on you go.

You fail once, you fail twice, and still you don't give in.

You know that every time you fail a new chance can begin.

You're steadfast in your firm belief that triumph will be yours,

Even if that means you slightly redirect your course.

Your goal is like a peak, with more than one path to the top.

It doesn't matter which you take, as long as you don't stop.

By never giving up no matter how hard things may get,

You'll find what you are looking for. You'll rarely find regret.

Q is for quiet – it's too rarely found:

An absence of chatter, a respite from sound.

The quiet provides time to think and to rest.

To seek it each day is a laudable quest.

There's peace to discover when silence is sought.

Serenity follows the stillness of thought.

A calmness encircles the quieted brain,

An uplifting feeling you hope to retain.

When you sit in silence, your mind takes a break

From noise that intrudes from the moment you wake.

Free from disturbance, you'll find it relaxing.

Quiet gives shelter when life gets too taxing.

R's for reliable: when you do what you should.

You don't say you can't when you said that you would.

You want to be trusted to finish a charge,

So you don't give up and claim it was too large.

The quality found in the work that you do

Will tell people all they should know about you.

Responsible actions will help you stand out.

Accomplishing tasks is what you are about.

There's value in knowing on whom to depend.

Go forth as the one who is true to the end.

When you are committed to keeping your word

No task is too great; you will be undeterred.

S for spontaneous – a drive from within.

You act on your urges; you act on a whim.

In playing out happy-go-lucky desires,

You give to your spirit the joy it requires.

It's not an excuse to be reckless or brash

Or act in a way that will make you seem rash.

But not all decisions demand over thinking.

You might find it fun to jump in and risk sinking.

Those spur-of-the-moment and unplanned events

Can offer relief when life gets too intense.

Open yourself up to your inclinations,

And follow your dreams; go without reservations.

T is for tolerance: having the gift
To bear what is different without getting miffed.
It's having an impartial attitude towards
Traditions and views that may differ from yours.
It's possible that you could learn something great
With patience for those who at times deviate.

It's often the thing that is not like the rest
That isn't just better; it's really the best.
Accept those in life who aren't part of the norm.
The truly unique should not have to conform.
When tolerance reigns and acceptance succeeds
The world will, at last, find the peace that it needs.

27

U's for unique; a description you'll find

That says you're entirely one of a kind!

Those uncommon traits that are found just in you

Are good things to recognize -- celebrate, too.

Let that which is different about you stand out.

Allow it to flourish; don't let it cause doubt.

With faith in your specialness you'll be secure.

With that there is nothing you cannot endure.

There may be some people, they're part of the norm,

Who'll try to convince you that you should conform.

But when you find comfort in just who you are,

You'll unearth the power to shine like a star.

V is for vocabulary. Once you learn to talk

You'll need it in the manner that you need your legs to walk.

It's ALL the words, not some of them, but all the words you know,

A list that started right at birth and through the years should grow.

Through pictures on the walls of caves the cavemen once opined.

Then letters came along and so our words became refined.

When sharing thoughts, the words you know will help you to express

The point you want to get across. So do it with finesse.

Communication's vital for the human race to run.

Ideas kept in silence do no good for anyone.

When you know lots of words you'll find you have much more to say.

The world respects intelligence, and words will guide the way.

W's for wisdom, it means having common sense.

Applying knowledge that's been gained through life experience.

For you to make decisions that will help your life go far,

You might begin by asking someone older than you are.

Observing those who always seem to know just what to do

Will help enhance the wisdom that is growing within you.

Good judgment is the wise man's tool; it also must be learned.

The insight to discern what's best is something that is earned.

Accumulating knowledge is the best way to proceed.

And then at your disposal you'll have data you may need.

Assess the world around you, understand its lows and highs.

And then make good decisions that reflect how you are wise.

X is not for anything....You know that isn't true!

But mostly X will follow E, so here's a list for you.

Exacerbate is when you make a bad thing even worse.

Extinct means something's gone for good, a deed you can't reverse.

Excluding is to leave somebody out and all alone.

Express means setting forth in words the thoughts that you want known.

Exuberance is overflowing joy you can't suppress.

Excel means that you do extremely well to reach success.

Explore means to investigate, examine what's around.

Exquisite means a thing's so fine its beauty will astound.

It's strange that words can start the same but end up so diverse.

There's magic in the language of our awesome universe.

Y is for yourself, the one who's always there for you.

Without yourself you couldn't do the things you love to do.

Your character, your nature, and your personality

Are all the things that strengthen your unique identity.

It's vital that you be yourself; no one else can do it.

And if you're feeling gloomy, help yourself to pull right through it.

Behave in ways that warrant self-respect and well-earned pride,

And work on changing attributes that make you want to hide.

Just never change yourself to please another. In the end,

When someone wants to change your YOU, they really aren't your friend.

You, yourself, and only you can build you or can break you.

No matter how you're treated, in the end it's you who'll make you.

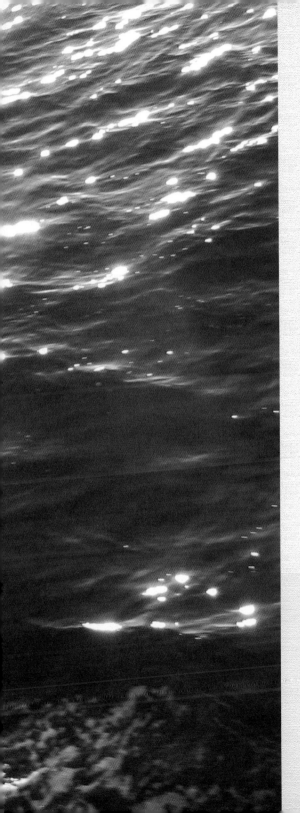

Z is for zest, it's vivacious delight.

The spark in your life that makes everything right.

It's outright elation and joy that you feel

When life feels good and it's wonderfully real.

It's there when you jump up and shout out "Wahoo!"

To those who will listen—or when it's just you.

You can't even say why you feel such pleasure.

Your bliss is abundant. You can't even measure

The thrill that you find in just everyday being

Alive and with people you just enjoying seeing.

Zest is the thing that makes life worth the hassle.

It makes you the king with the world as your castle.

Please use these pages to write down ways in which you intend to enact the essence of the words you've just read. Action helps to build comprehension.

_____

_____

_____

_____

_____

_____

_____

_____

_____

_____

Acknowledgements

Sincere appreciation to Gabriel Knight, whose creative eye provided many of the photos that make each word even more magnificent.

A big shout out to Francisco, Joe, Liz, and Vance, who each supplied a photo to enhance these pages.

And immense gratitude to Mary, whose precision and honesty reignited our enthusiasm for Magnificent Words, which had been placed on the back burner for much too long.

About The Authors

Laurie Gaboardi—*The Litchfield County Times*

Hamilton Brower is the favorite uncle of six nephews and three nieces. He worked for many years in New York City in the advertising industry as an Account Director. *Magnificent Words to Live By* represents an enormous accomplishment in Hamilton's life. Not only is this his first book written and published, but it also serves as a testament to mankind's ability to persevere: by seeing an idea through from one's imagination all the way to the printed and published page.

Annette Parker Martin is a happily married mother of three wonderful boys. Having held a diverse selection of jobs before and during college, she graduated with a degree in English with a concentration in writing. After college, she worked in the publishing industry before putting her career on hold to raise her sons with her husband, Jeff. Now that the boys are older and more independent, Annette has eagerly jumped back into the role of writer. This is also Annette's first book.